Use these stickers for the activities in the book

Page 2

Page 5

Page 8

Page 7

Page 12

Page 11

Page 11

pillow

picture

patchwork

Well done!

Well done!

Well done!

Well done!

Well done!

Well done!

Well done!

Page 15

ou ou ou ou

Pages 16–17

a a a a a a a a

Page 19

sl sn sn st

Page 21

w w w w w

Page 22

f f f f f

Page 24

snack

garden

table apple

fork fire

coat

picture

mouse

Well done!

Reading Together

Snow White
and the Seven Dwarfs

Phonics Consultant: Susan Purcell
Illustrator: Natalia Moore
Concept: Fran Bromage

Miles Kelly

As you read aloud, focus on the b sound (as in born)

Once upon a time, a beautiful baby girl was born to a king and queen. They named her Snow White.

But sadly the queen died before the baby was a year old.

Say the words as you spot each thing beginning with b.

Stick on their stickers.

baby

beard

boot

The king married again, but his new wife was mean.

She had a magic mirror, to which she would say,

"Mirror, mirror on the wall, who is the fairest of them all?"

"My lady, you are the fairest of them all," the mirror replied.

What a good try! Put a gold star here.

Sound out these words beginning with the m sound.

map **moth** **milk**

moon **market** **monster**

3

Focus on the
ee sound
(as in queen)

The mean queen always heard the same answer from the mirror.

But when Snow White was sixteen, the mirror replied,

"My queen, you are very fair – but Snow White seems to be the fairest of them all."

Sound out these words with the **ee** sound.

beat   team   clean

deep   sleep   cheese   teeth

4

The queen was green with envy.
She ordered a huntsman to seek
out Snow White and take her
deep into the forest.

Use your stickers to **spell** some more words with the **ee** sound.

bean   heat   tree   seen

Point out the ar sound (as in arm) as you read

The huntsman took Snow White by the arm, but did her no harm. He told her to run far away.

Sound out these words with the ar sound.

part   star   market

sharp   cart   dark   garden

6

Alarmed, Snow White ran far into the wood.

She was starting to feel tired, when she saw a charming cottage.

Use your stickers to **spell** some more words with the **ar** sound.

barn   p ary   far n   sma t

Snow White tapped on the door and tiptoed in. Everything inside was very tiny and terribly tidy.

Say the words as you spot things beginning with t.

Stick on their stickers.

8

teacup

table

teaspoon

Against the wall, Snow White saw seven small beds.

She yawned and walked over for a rest on one of them.

Well done!

Sound out these words with the or sound.

fork   short   hall   talk

chalk   crawl   draw

Hours later, when Snow White awoke, she wasn't alone.

She did not know she was in the home of seven dwarfs. They all spoke kindly to her.

Sound out these words, which all have the **oa** sound.

show   yellow   coat   boat

hole   rope   broke

"Perhaps you'd like to stay," said a dwarf in a purple hat, popping up near the bed.

Use your arrow stickers to **point** to some things that begin with p.

Well done!

Use your stickers to **spell** some words beginning with the p sound.

pen   pond   put   park   pink

So, each day as the seven dwarfs set off for work Snow White fussed over them and made them sandwiches.

Say the words as you spot each thing with the s sound.

 **Stick on** their stickers.

glasses

grass

dress

Meanwhile, one night the magic mirror told the evil queen that Snow White was still alive.

"You lie!" cried the queen with all her might.

Sound out these words, which all use the ie sound.

high   fight   light

pie   tie   ice   mile   time

The queen was so annoyed! Snow White was spoiling her plan to be the fairest in the land.

So, the queen poisoned an apple, disguised her face and voice, and set off to join Snow White.

Sound out these words with the oi sound.

boy   toy   enjoy

oi   coin   soil   point

14

She found Snow White safe and sound in the dwarfs' house.

"Apples for sale!" shouted the queen, with a frown.

Emphasize the ow sound (as in frown)

Use the stickers to **spell** some words with the **ow** sound.

ab**ou**t   m**ou**nt   h**ou**nd   m**ou**se

The queen began to eat one side of an apple.

You can have this one.

But it wasn't the bad, poisoned part. The queen handed the apple to Snow White.

Use your stickers to **spell** some words with the **a** sound.

ant   **a**dd   m**a**n   c**a**p   r**a**t

16

Snow White began to eat the poisoned side of the apple. After one bite, she fell down as if dead!

Use your stickers to **complete** the sentence with the a sound.

Snow White began to eat the apple.

When the dwarfs returned, they were startled to see Snow White lying on the ground. She lay as **still** as a **stone**.

Sound out these words, which have sl, sn and st blends.

slug   slipper   snap   sneeze

stuff   step   story

The dwarfs **sn**atched up the apple and realised Snow White had been poisoned.

Stunned, they **sl**owly placed Snow White in a glass case, and **st**ood it in the woods.

Use your stickers to **spell** some words with the sl, sn and st blends.

slide   **sn**ack   **sn**ore   **st**ung

As you read, focus on the h sound (as in hand)

One day, a handsome prince rode past. As he leant over to look at Snow White he knocked the glass case.

The horrible piece of apple flew out of her mouth, and she opened her eyes.

Say the names of the things with the h sound, as you spot them.

horse   hair   head

hedge   hand

The prince asked Snow White to be his wife.

The wedding was wonderful, and the dwarfs wished them well.

Try to emphasize the w sound (as in was)

Use your stickers to **spell** these words, which all use the w sound.

wet   way   won   wish   web

There was no happy ending for the queen.

"Who is the fairest of them all?" she asked her mirror for the final time.

When she heard 'Snow White' she was so full of fury, she caught fire and vanished!

Use your stickers to **spell** some words beginning with f.

fed   fish   fog   fast   fur

Ask your child to **retell** the story using
these key sounds and story images.

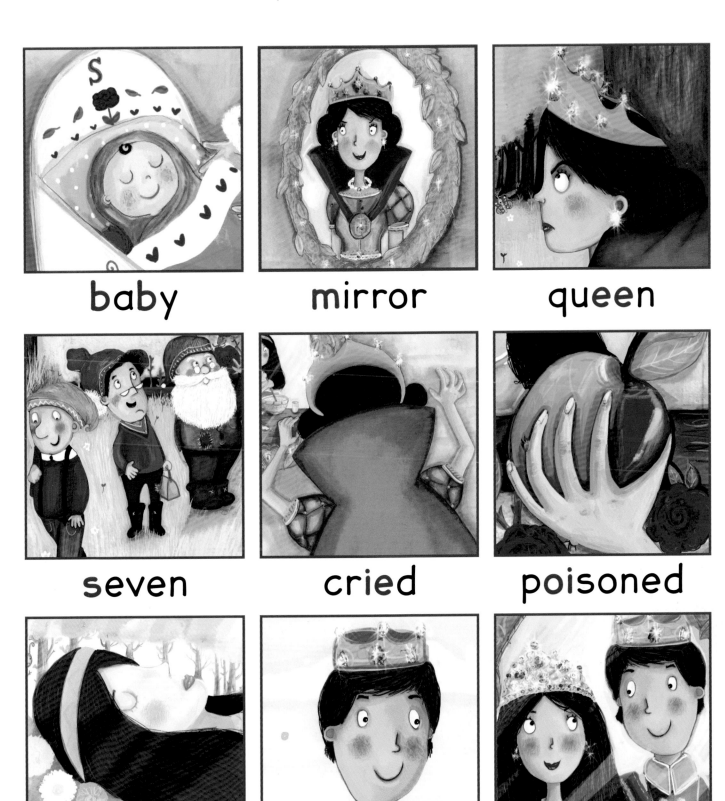

baby

mirror

queen

seven

cried

poisoned

still

handsome

wedding

Use your stickers to **add** a word that matches
the red highlighted **sounds** on each line.

far   part   farm

tidy   tiny   teacup

short   talk   crawl

snow   know   alone

pond   pink   pillow

frown   house   shout

ant   man   rat

snore   sneeze   snap

full   fury   fast

24

You've had fun with phonics! Well done.